B.C. Where The Hell is Heck?

Johnny Hart

CORONET BOOKS
Hodder Fawcett, London

© 1973 Publishers Newspaper Syndicate
© 1978 CBS Publications, The Consumer
Publishing Division of CBS Inc.

First published in the United States of America
by Fawcett Gold Medal

Coronet edition 1980

Printed in Great Britain for Hodder
Fawcett Ltd., Mill Road, Dunton Green,
Sevenoaks, Kent (Editorial Office: 47
Bedford Square, London, WC1 3DP) by
Hunt Barnard Printing Ltd.,
Aylesbury, Bucks.

ISBN 0 340 25066 6

JAKE, WHY DON'T YOU EXPLAIN SPORTS TO ME...

..THEN MAYBE NEXT YEAR I WON'T BE A SUNDAY AFTERNOON WIDOW.

OK! .... THE FIRST THING WE'LL TAKE UP IS THE TIGHT END.

1·30

WAS THAT THE FAT GUY AT THE END OF THE COUCH THAT THREW UP DURING THE SUPER BOWL ?....

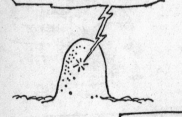

2-7

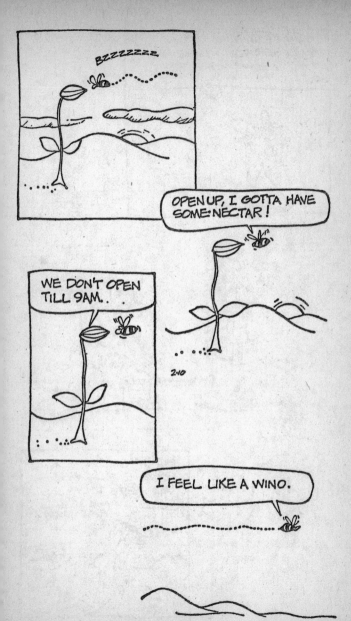

2

2-21

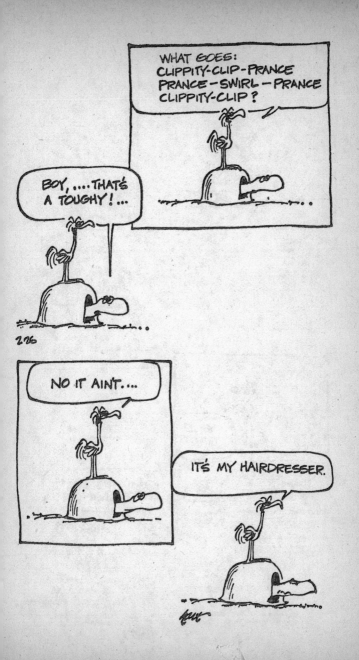

3

3.7

3·13

3-14

3·21

Dear Fat Broad,
Part of my neighbor's
fig tree hangs over my fence
and ruins my grass...

ADVICE COLUMN

3·29

...what would happen if I
were to cut off his limbs?

— aggressive.

DEAR AGGRESSIVE,
HE WOULD HAVE TO HIRE
SOMEONE TO PICK HIS FIGS.

ADVICE COLUMN

Dear Fat Broad,
My husband left me 3 yrs.
ago, and I haven't seen
hide nor hair of him since,

3·30

who do I contact?
— anxious.

DEAR ANXIOUS,
...EITHER DR. JEKYLL OR
PETER RABBIT.

4·10

4·24

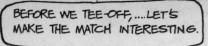

426

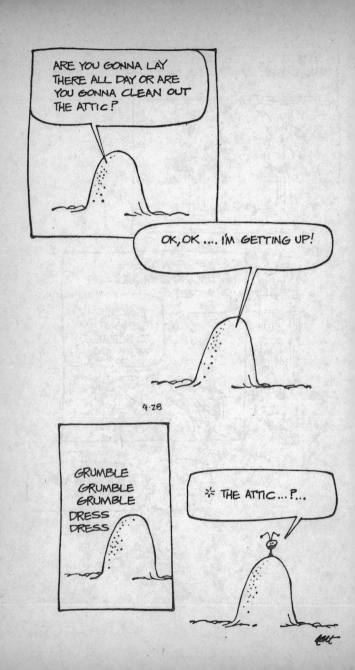

5·5

5.9

5-11

5.18

5-21

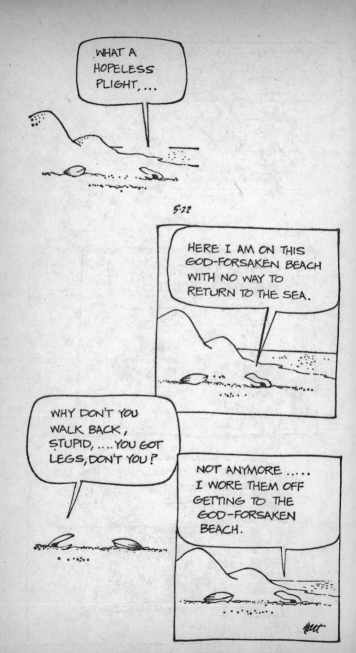

GOOD MORNING MR. FROG, I'M YOUR "MAN IN THE STREET" FROM STATION W·A·N·T,..

5·23

OUR QUESTION TODAY IS: WHAT DO FROGS DO WHEN PROVOKED TO THE POINT OF ....

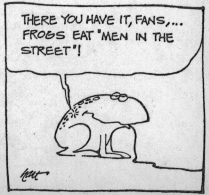

THERE YOU HAVE IT, FANS,... FROGS EAT "MEN IN THE STREET"!

6.6

big·a·mist *n.*

an Italian's description of his last visit to London.

one who goes out on the golf
course as an assigned risk.

LOOK, LOOK, SEE DICK and JANE PLAN THEIR VACATION.

OH, LOOK, SEE THEM PLACE SPOT and PUFF IN THE KENNELS.

SEE THE KENNEL MASTER LAY HIS FEE ON DICK and JANE

6-25

SEE DICK and JANE SPEND THEIR VACATION VISITING SPOT and PUFF.

LOOK, LOOK, SEE DICK and JANE ROUGHING IT IN "YELLOWSTONE"

627

SEE DICK and JANE RUN OUT OF SUPPLIES.

SEE DICK and JANE IN THEIR BEAR SUITS BEGGING FOOD FROM the CARS.

SEE DICK and JANE GET
LOST IN THE WOODS.

6·29

SEE DICK SAVE THE DAY BY
REMEMBERING HIS COMPASS

SEE DICK and JANE SPEND
THEIR LAST DAYS MAKING
LITTLE CIRCLES IN THE DIRT.

SEE DICK RENT THE
SPEEDBOAT
SEE JANE RENT THE
WATERSKIS

SEE DICK and JANE
SPEED AWAY FROM
THE DOCK

6·30

SEE THE BOAT RUN
AGROUND

SEE THE DOC
EXTRACT JANE
FROM THE BACK
OF THE BOAT.

NO
SERVICES
THIS
ROUTE

7·3

EVEN THE CHURCH IS
SUFFERING CUTBACKS.

big·a·mous *n.*

WILEY'S DICTIONARY

7·4

an Italian's excuse for forcing a three-pound wedge of cheese into a mouse-trap.

WILEY'S DICTIONARY

7·6

1·1

LOOK, LOOK, SEE
DICK GO ON A SAFARI

SEE THE BEATERS AND
BEARERS CALL DICK
"BWANA."

7.10

SEE THE LION CHARGE
DICK.
SEE DICK APPEAL TO
THE BEATERS and BEARERS
FOR HELP

SEE DICK
DISCOVER WHAT
"BWANA" REALLY
MEANS.

7-7

SEE DICK AND JANE SHED
THEIR WORLDLY BELONGINGS

SEE DICK AND JANE GO
BACK TO NATURE

723

SEE THE RANGER ARREST
DICK AND JANE FOR GOING
BACK TOO FAR.

OH, LOOK, SEE DICK BUILD A CAMPFIRE.

SEE DICK FORGET TO PUT THE CAMPFIRE OUT

7·24

SEE SMOKEY SNUFF OUT THE FIRE WITH DICK'S FACE.

THIS IS IT, COACH, ... I'M HANGING UP MY SPIKES.

YOU'RE QUITTING BASEBALL?

7.30

NO, I'M GIVING UP RAILROAD COMMERCIALS.

hart

83

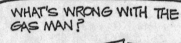

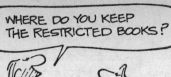

94

8

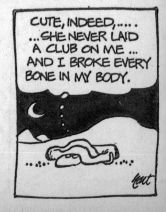

HI, JAKE....

9.17

HOW DID YOU LIKE THE
PEANUT BUTTER AND
MOLASSES SANDWICH
I PUT IN YOUR LUNCH PAIL
TODAY?

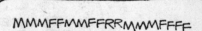

MMMFFMMFFRRMMMFFFF

u.25

96

CORONET CARTOONS

JOHNNY HART

☐ 18820 0	B.C. on the Rocks	50p
☐ 19474 X	B.C. Right On	60p
☐ 19873 7	B.C. Cave In	60p
☐ 20653 5	B.C. One More Time	50p
☐ 16477 8	Back to B.C.	60p
☐ 16881 1	What's New B.C.	60p
☐ 21784 7	Life is a 60p Paperback	60p

JOHNNY HART AND BRANT PARKER

☐ 20529 6	Long Live the King	60p
☐ 20776 0	Wizard of Id Yield	60p
☐ 18604 6	There's a Fly in My Swill	50p
☐ 23845 3	Wizard of Id: Help Stamp Out Grapes	60p
☐ 23017 7	Wizard of Id: Let There Be Reign	60p

All these books are available at your local bookshop or newsagent, or can be ordered direct from the publisher. Just tick the titles you want and fill in the form below.

Prices and availability subject to change without notice.

CORONET BOOKS, P.O. Box 11, Falmouth, Cornwall.

Please send cheque or postal order, and allow the following for postage and packing:

U.K. – One book 25p plus 10p per copy for each additional book ordered, up to a maximum of £1.05.

B.F.P.O. and EIRE – 25p for the first book plus 10p per copy for the next 8 books, thereafter 5p per book.

OTHER OVERSEAS CUSTOMERS – 40p for the first book and 12p per copy for each additional book.

Name ....

Address ....

....